I have never met Johnny Hart and I don't know that I care to. I say that not in genial kidding, but with the same sincerity that Rita Hayworth might say it about Tuesday Weld.

I am sort of the Rita Hayworth of the comic page and Johnny Hart is the Tuesday Weld. I am a long-established beauty, so damn long-established that it gets tougher every day to maintain my (blush!!!) beauty. I have to use all sorts of tricks and subterfuges and be sure the lighting is right, so as not to reveal crowsfeet in my story line, or sagging gags.

Now Johnny Hart being the fresh, young, new, vibrant Tuesday Weld of our profession doesn't need to worry and work to make an impression, or his stuff doesn't reveal that he does. He simply seems to have it. A few joyous lines, a few marvelously chosen words, and the crowd is cheering. When I think of the sweat and blood I pour to get the same effect — but — oh — the hell with that — this is Johnny Hart's book, and it's full of his genius, and if you happen not to be an older and envious cartoonist, you're going to have a very good time.

—AL CAPP.

Creator of L'IL ABNER

BACK

# TO B.C.

## BY JOHNNY HART

A FAWCETT GOLD MEDAL BOOK

FAWCETT PUBLICATIONS, INC., GREENWICH, CONN.

MEMBER OF AMERICAN BOOK PUBLISHERS COUNCIL, INC.

Published by arrangement with G. P. Putnam's Sons.

Published by Fawcett World Library,
67 West 44th Street, New York, New York 10036
Printed in the United States of America.

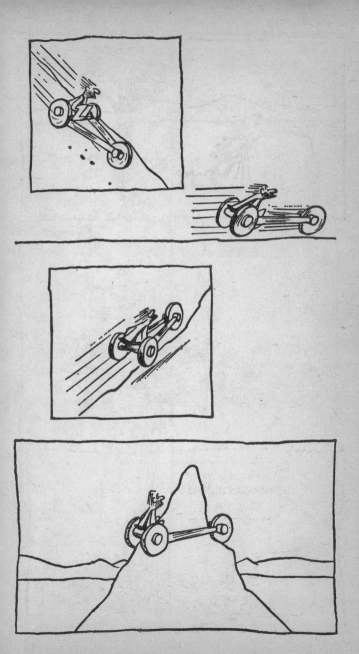

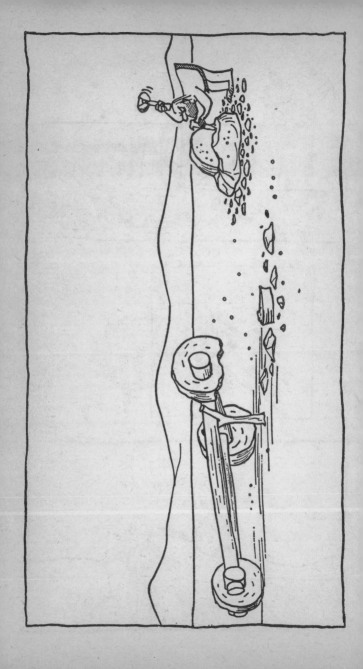

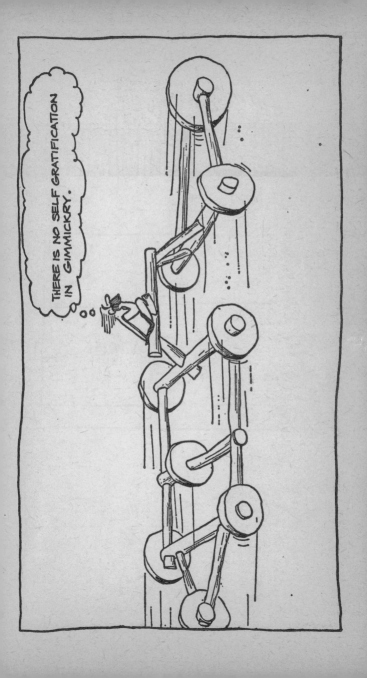

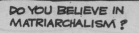

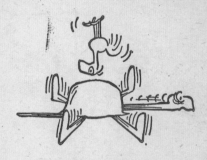

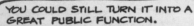

EVERYBODY THINKS HE CAN WRITE A BOOK.

MIGHTY BIG NOSE YOU HAVE THERE.
ANYONE EVER TELL YOU, YOU HAVE A SUNKEN CHEST ?
CAN'T YOU DO ANYTHING BUT FOLLOW PEOPLE AROUND?

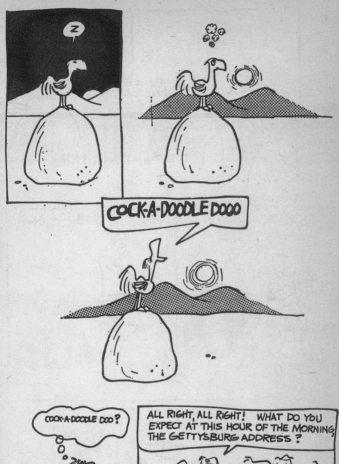

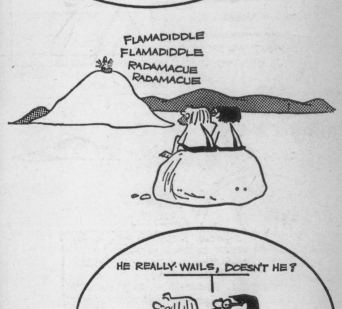

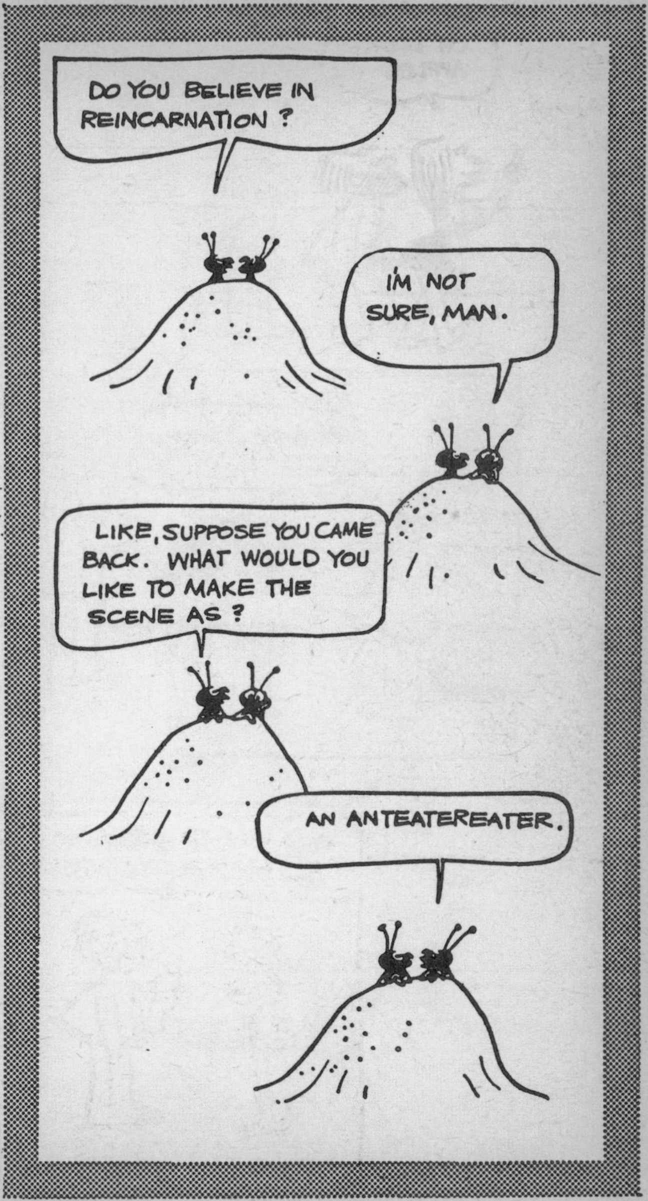
DO YOU BELIEVE IN REINCARNATION ?
I'M NOT SURE, MAN.
LIKE, SUPPOSE YOU CAME BACK. WHAT WOULD YOU LIKE TO MAKE THE SCENE AS ?
AN ANTEATEREATER.

LET'S SEE YOU THROW THE JAVELIN
WHAT WOULD YOU LIKE ME TO DO NEXT?
RUN FOR YOUR LIFE!

I AM ABOUT TO BUILD A JAIL, IN WHICH WE WILL PUNISH WRONGDOERS.
I'LL NEED YOU THREE TO HELP BUILD IT.
WHAT CAN I DO ?
YOU CAN THINK UP A BUNCH OF WRONGDOINGS.